MW00582336

Herding People: A Do-It-Yourself Guide for Cats

To Ann
with love,
and Will

By
Will Richan and Ampers

Copyright © 2022 Will Richan

All rights reserved.

ISBN:

Contents

Dedication

Dedicated to all those cat lovers out there and the felines
they think they own.

Acknowledgements

Many thanks to Rev. Joyce Tomkins, from whom we got Ampers in the first place, and to the cat ladies who look after Ampers when we're away, and to the folks at Providence Veterinary Hospital, who step in when needed.

About the Authors

You will become well acquainted with Ampers as you delve into Herding People.

Will Richan has written a number of textbooks, one of which went to three editions, and two novels. His writing career began as a radio news editor, where the priority, other than being factual, was to grab listeners' attention and keep them from turning the dial, all without the help of the visuals. That may help explain some reactions to the novels: "Couldn't stop reading."

A Note to the Reader

Ampers, our cat, should really get the credit for this book. It is totally his story, with me, Will, helping a little with the editing. First, a little background on Ampers: When we got him from a friend, we learned that his real name was Ampersand. Not hard to figure out where he got that moniker. Add a couple of ears and a few whiskers to an ampersand and, lo and behold, a sitting cat.

It didn't take long to discover what a gifted creature was our Ampers once I learned cat whispering. So he told me the story, and I sat at the computer, taking it all down. I offered to let him do the typing, but he said, "No thanks; never did like playing 'Kitten on the Keys.'"

Okay, I'll let him take it from there.

-Will Richan

Preface

Books about cats are a dime a dozen. Tending, coddling, and making fun of – that should give people a leg up when it comes to dealing with us. The trouble is, people, being a bit challenged in the smarts department, are constantly playing catch up with us. You might say we can run circles around humans, literally as well as figuratively.

So a book of, by, and for cats is long overdue. In this volume, we turn the tables and talk about ways of handling people. Here is a self-help guide for making sure that we stay in control of our human friends instead of the other way around.

Chapter 1 is intended to give you an appreciation of your true gifts, which is always a good first step in learning anything. The first thing is to get past the human-generated propaganda about us. Walk with pride, cat. Richly deserved.

In Chapter 2, we look at our long and distinguished heritage, going back to the earliest times when we first pretended to be domesticated.

It's a cat's life; you might say, so make the most out of it. In Chapter 3, we get into basic lifestyle issues. Not that your present life is all that great, but you should have an image of what life can be for us felines.

No matter what, if there's one thing we cats have, it's a sense of humor—nothing like a few practical jokes to put a little bounce in your stride. Chapter 4, in a way, is what herding people is all about.

In Chapter 5, we look at the problem of cohabitation with other species besides humankind. Unfortunately, many people who love cats also love dogs, canaries, fishes, and other obnoxious creatures. To say nothing of cats, you wouldn't want to be seen in public.

As is laid out in Chapter 6, there is a reason cats don't play baseball. Not that we wouldn't be great at snagging flies and totally befuddling opponents. To find out the real reason, you'll have to read the chapter.

Finally, of course, we could take over the world tomorrow. In Chapter 7, we look at why we don't. For starters, who would want all that responsibility? It is more fun to herd people, one household at a time.

Chapter 1: What Mitsou taught Marilyn Monroe

This chapter is about understanding your own strength, and I do mean brains. As a cat, you are far superior to animals that rate higher on the IQ scale, especially humans – but more about that later. So, the first thing to do is put aside everything you thought you knew about cats and smarts.

Are you really dumber than pigs, parrots, and dogs? Humans who claim to know about such things say yes. Then how come you're the only species that can be owned by humans and simultaneously run their lives?

Let's start with brain size. The so-called experts say the bigger the brain compared with body weight, the smarter the species; that's just human propaganda. Having the biggest brain/weight ratio around, they have perpetuated that myth. Talk about swell heads!

So, okay, cats have a brain the size of a pea. The truth is, size is no measure of anything, take computers as an example. When they first appeared on the scene, it took a room full of monsters to do anything useful. Today, a slim disk (the size of that pea I was talking about a moment ago) can do things way beyond their ancestors' comprehension.

The real point is that it's not the so-called intelligence that matters but what one does with it. Humans are finally catching on to that basic fact that cats have known for eons. Take educators, for example. Let's say Child 1 has an IQ in the genius class, totally lacks self-discipline, and is convinced he/she can't do the math, reading, and other stuff. Other than that, Child 2 has an IQ score in the middle of the pack, but he treats a poor grade on a quiz as a sign that he/she didn't try hard enough. Failure is a challenge to try harder. So, whereas Child 1 gives up on the spot, Child 2 picks himself up out of the dust and keeps going. That's the one I would bet my Greenies on. It's not just me saying it. Educators are saying the same thing. Check it out the next time you're on the computer (no, silly, not literally on top of the console, I mean sitting in front of the thing playing your version of 'Kitten on the Keys.')

This brings us to Mitsou and Marilyn Monroe. Beautiful, blonde, vivacious, shapely, using her body to great advantage, etc. No, I'm not talking about Marilyn. I'm talking about Mitsou: a beautiful Persian feline that Ms. Monroe lived with in the mid-fifties in New York City.

The timing is important. Mitsou arrived while the so-called Blonde Bombshell was worrying about getting typecast in 'dumb blonde' roles. Monroe wanted to be seen as a serious actress. She actually managed to turn in some stellar performances. That's when Mitsou stepped in and gave her a piece of advice:

"You got it all wrong," said the cat one day when they were watching reruns of some of MM's early films. Yes, our Marilyn was a cat whisperer on the side.

"You got to play dumb, honey," said Mitsou. "Besides, it's so much fun to see directors tearing out what remains of their hair."

About that time, when they were getting ready to shoot Some Like It Hot, casting Marilyn as a stereotypical dumb blonde named Sugar. It's not just that MM carried off the assignment so well that she got a Golden Globe out of it. What's more interesting is the way she managed to drive director Billy Wilder a bit wilder.

In one scene, she is supposed to ask, "Where's the bourbon?" and then find it in a bureau drawer. The retakes they needed for that set some kind of record. "Where's the whiskey?" and "Where's the bon-bon?" and other fumbled lines were carried off peerlessly. And then there was the search through bureau drawers. She must have hit every one of them before she got to the right one. Human commentators are still pointing back at that one as evidence that MM had some empty spaces in the attic, which shows how dumb humans can be, especially film critics.

"I'm proud of you, kid," said Mitsou after that caper.

Cats have been playing this game since time began, or at least since cats started pretending to be domesticated—more on that subject in the next chapter.

"No, sweet one, not on the dining table while we're eating." Followed by another lithe leap and another rejoinder. And another.

"Oh dear, another hairball on the living room carpet." And another a few days later. "No, naughty kitty. We don't pee on the bathmat, Cuddles. Remember your litter box? That's a good girl."

I've heard that cats are one of the leading causes of divorce but haven't been able to find a reliable source.

The trick is to make humans think it's because of the pea-sized brain. Dogs, being more trainable, are automatically assumed to be smarter than cats. They are farther up the brain chain, to be sure. But, whereas felines are #10 and canines are #6 on the list, pigs are #2. Talk about dumb. Pigs ought to know by this time that they have one purpose in life, one that's not too cool if you happen to be a pig. Why they didn't introduce people to pig milk a long time ago, I'll never know.

So, be happy that you're grossly underestimated. Playing dumb definitely has advantages. It means that nobody really runs your life except you. As we'll see later, that includes cats who've made it to the White House—ignoring the pleas of US presidents and their families. Does it get any better than that?

Chapter 2: A Long and Proud Heritage

It took a long time for humans to show their appreciation for cats, but it finally happened in 2002, when August 8 was set aside as International Cat Day by the International Fund for Animal Welfare. In this country, it wasn't until 2005 that National Cat Day made it onto the calendar. Bet you don't even know when it's celebrated. October 29, that's when. But as usual, countries can't agree about most things. Many European countries observed World Cat Day on February 17. In Russia, it's March 1. So there are plenty of opportunities to recognize us. Take pride, cats.

It hasn't been easy - the being proud part, I mean. Take what happened with Noah and his ark. Sure, he let us aboard, but we were The Great Unclean - which puts us in a category like the Untouchables of the old Indian caste system. It had its advantages, needless to say, since "unclean" meant "not to be eaten."

It didn't take Noah and his family long to discover they needed us, not with all those rats and mice running all over the craft. That's us: necessary but not really appreciated.

O.K., history means dates: You know, what year did something or other happens? Problem one: How do you figure dates? Answer: It all depends. It's all because people have such a hard time agreeing on anything or even staying with a decision once it's made. No wonder humans have things in such a muddle.

Which takes us back to the reckoning of years. Once upon a time, Christians said a year was either B.C. (Before Christ) or A.D. (Anno Domini, or Year of Our Lord). Then they changed their minds and started using B.C.E. (Before the Common Era) and C.E. (Common Era). They expected everybody to go along with the new designations.

Never mind that for Jews, 2022 C.E. might really be 5786, depending on the time of year. Not all Jews, you understand. Or 1439 if you are a Muslim. The Chinese, on the other hand, might say it's 4714. Some Chinese that is. Others might be saying 4654. What a mess!

Cats have no such problem. We go by B.G.E., and T.G.E. B.G.E. is Before the Great Enslavement. T.G.E. is the Time of the Great Enslavement. What is the year 2022 C.E., in terms of T.G.E.? I don't have the remotest idea. Nor do I care, really. One year is like another for us cats.

But the Great Enslavement? Now that's quite a different matter. Before then, every human who was anything was a hunter-gatherer. Unless, of course, you were a king, queen, Pharoah, or something like that.

Hunter-gatherers spent their time chasing down wild boars and saber-toothed tigers and such, not to mention getting chased down in return. That was the men mostly. The women, meanwhile, were out trying to get to the fruit and nuts before the birds and squirrels did.

Then somebody got the bright idea of planting seeds in the ground and becoming farmers. Now the only problem, besides occasional droughts and floods, was to get to the harvest before the mice and rats did. By then, people realized there was somebody who did a far better job of catching the little demons than they did. You guessed it, cats.

That's when The Great Enslavement began. Still going on, of course. Not that our slavery even begins to compare with what the man slaves have gone through, but we could have used a little help from old Honest Abe when he was freeing those other slaves. But not only did he have a tin ear when it came to cat emancipation. He had the gall to have his portrait taken at least once with a cat sitting on his lap— more on that in a moment.

No, it soon became evident that we were on our own when it came to fighting for feline freedom. That's when we figured out how to turn a disaster into a win-win situation.

The first thing you have to do when you enslave somebody is to define that creature as a lesser being. That supposedly makes it all right to do the enslaving. I must say it is a bit demoralizing for the slaves, but, as illustrated in Chapter 1, it can have its advantages.

But not to dwell on that dark chapter in our history, we cats have been close to the seat of power - in fact, in the seat of power. You don't get much closer than the White House.

Life in and around the Oval Office:

Cats were really insulted when Honest Abe left us out of that Emancipation Proclamation bit. He thought it was enough to let Tabby live in the White House. We're still proud of Tabby, though: first to make it into the place. That's the thing about firsts, of course: They remember you for being the first something-or-other, and that's supposed to be enough. Too easy to be nothing but a photo op. Take Tabby, for instance. When they wanted Lincoln to sit for an official photo, he'd insist on dragging Tabby up on his lap. So big deal, huh? Sit there for a few seconds and off to hunt mice, right? Wrong. In those days, getting your portrait taken meant freezing in place for what seemed like hours while the photographer fiddled around with his lenses, etc. Especially if it's for an official pic of el Numero Primo.

Back to the slavery thing. Tabby, who could identify with all those folks being persecuted on plantations, kept warning old Abe that he wasn't going far enough. The guy wouldn't listen; he can't push too hard, he'd say. Got to let the people catch up. After that, things got a little cooler between Tabby and his - ahem - master.

After Lincoln was assassinated, there was a nasty rumor going around that cats had been in on the plot. Accused Tabby of knowing something and not warning the Prez. No way. We may be devious, but no cat would sink to that level. They let Tabby attend the funeral, but he had to promise to stay out of sight. One more insult to catdom.

Rutherford B. Hayes was the next President to bring a cat into the White House. Siam, as her name suggests, was an immigrant from the country of the same name. Not only did she help to break down the prejudice against Asians, but she was treated like royalty. Wherever Mrs. Hayes went in public, Siam was sure to be close by.

Speaking of that Asian immigrant thing, Siam convinced President Hayes - rather, convinced Mrs. Hayes, who got to the old man - not to go along with the pressure to bar Chinese and other Asians from entering the country. President Hayes, to whom Chinese and Siamese were sort of the same thing ("They don't look like us"), refused to join the ethnocentric clamor. Result: The Chinese Exclusion Act didn't get passed until it was signed into law by Hayes's successor, Chester Allen Arthur.

If Siam had lived long enough, she might have headed off the whole thing. But alas, she died of food poisoning. That's the official version, at least. The Secretary of Agriculture was supposed to preserve her remains for posterity, but there's no trace of old Siam anywhere in the Department of Agriculture Museum or the Smithsonian. Foul play? Hmm. But who knows? We'll have to let that be one of history's unsolved mysteries.

William McKinley and his family had a penchant for giving cats exotic names: Valeriano Weyler was named after the Governor of Cuba, and Enrique De Leon got his name from the Spanish ambassador. Both gentlemen were insulted, especially when the President refused to let their feline namesakes live in the White House.

It turned out that was a very unwise decision. You see, cats know a lot more than they let on. Not that anybody would have listened if they had passed along the rumors about a zealous anarchist out to knock off the Prez, but at least the cats could have tried. As it was, the assassination of the old man didn't cause much weeping in the cat world.

Teddy Roosevelt, who took over from McKinley, apparently paid attention. Slippers had the run of the place, which was a source of irritation to some dinner guests, who sometimes had to step around the sleeping feline on the way to the trough. Slippers had another mark of distinction: the only six-toed cat in White House history.

The other Roosevelt feline acquisition was Tom Quartz, who is remembered for little except that he was named after a cat in one of Mark Twain's opuses. But then, considering how Roosevelt treated some of our distant cousins - mounting their heads on the wall alongside water buffalo and such - obscurity has its advantages.

The only problem for Slippers and Tom Quartz was the number of other creatures with which they had to share the White House. A raft of children, of course. And you know children. It's no accident they were called the White House Gang. But then there were no fewer than nine dogs, a garter snake, a pony, a pig, a badger, a rat (never could nail that monster), some number of guinea pigs, a hen, a macaw, a rooster, and a pony. Not all were kept in the White House, of course. But such an infernal din going far into the night! And some of these guys never heard of litter boxes, apparently. Phew!

Woodrow Wilson had a cat named Puffins. I'm guessing the only reason was to keep the mice in check. That's because, if nothing else, the President was utilitarian when it came to animals. A herd of sheep, for example, he saw as an economical way to keep the White House lawn trimmed. The chickens? Well, you guess that one. But being a son of the South, we'd have to guess that when it came to culinary delights, fried chicken was right up there.

When it came to favorite pets, Wilson was a dog lover, but he did have one trait in common with cats: You will notice that whenever you see a picture of our 28th President, he's never smiling. Despite what Lewis Carroll wrote about the Cheshire cat, we do not smile. We purr instead. Also, use our tails to express joy, sorrow, anger, fear, etc.

Of Calvin Coolidge, the less said, the better. According to legend, I can believe, as a lad he took great pleasure in stowing the family cat in the hall clock or on a porch roof, freeing the poor creature only when its pitiful meows could be resisted longer.

On the day of his inauguration in 1925, Mr. Coolidge whiled away the time before embarking on the Presidential cavalcade by putting a cat in a crate with a rooster, just to see what would happen.

Once in the White House, Coolidge acquired two kittens, Tige (for Tiger, of course) and Blacky. On some occasions, he would appear with Tige draped around his neck like an old scarf. Clearly not the cat's idea of fun. Tige finally made his escape, never to be seen again. As for the other feline, Blacky avoided the Prez altogether and hid out in the kitchen.

Despite the fact that he came out of nowhere to step into Franklin D. Roosevelt's big shoes after FDR died in office, Harry Truman was not a friend of cats. He once had the audacity to say, "If you want a friend in Washington, get a dog." So much for HST.

Fast forward to the sixties. The Kennedys had Tom Kitten. Cute name but a big problem. It turned out our President had an allergy to cats. The first time Tom K got his dander up (literally), that was it.

One mark of distinction: Tom was the only White House cat to have his own obituary in the daily press. He died in 1962, so I never got to read the President's.

Gerald Ford, who was more or less a footnote to history anyway, never had a cat of his own that we know of. Daughter Susan had a Siamese cat named Shan. Never reached the heights of the first White House Siamese, the one owned by R.B. Hayes. But still close enough to the seat of power to warrant a mention.

Want a fancy cat name? How about Misty Malarky Ying Yang? I kid you not. Try saying that fast three times without taking a breath. Owned Jimmy Carter's daughter Amy. That's not a typo, incidentally. Humans got to learn whose boss. Why do they do that to cats?

Ronald Reagan is remembered as a decent, people kind of guy, his policies notwithstanding. So it's not surprising, I suppose, that he and Nancy took in strays from time to time: Cleo and Sara, plus a number of others, didn't even have the dignity of a name. Not White House cats, you understand; they were all kept down on el rancho.

Of all the White House cats, probably none is better remembered than Socks, Chelsea Clinton's pal. Young Chelsea was on her way home from a piano lesson, so the story goes, when she stopped to play with some abandoned kittens in a park. Socks leaped up into her arms. Chelsea, sensing that this was a stray in need of a home, decided on the spot to become a first responder.

Socks was a celebrity in his own right: movies, TV, a book or two, a secretary to handle his email, limo rides on the way to important functions. Since nobody in catdom knew his birthday, we've had to settle for his death day (February 20). If you are a cat lover, you should check a feline friend out on that date. So perhaps a bit of extra meowing. For some of us, it's a fast day so the kitty may be less interested in the old food dish than usual.

I'll have more to say about Socks and his arch-rival, Buddy, Bill Clinton's Lab, in Chapter 5.

India, George W. Bush's cat, was a second-class citizen from the start. On the other hand, Barney, his black Scotty, was constantly in the public eye. On top of everything else, there was outrage among Indians (the Southeast Asia kind) for having a cat named after their country. Some folks can be touchy about the darnedest things.

Maybe because Bush was a little contrite after showering so much attention on Barny, he did several paintings of cats, including one of India. Did a decent job of it, too. Nice to know he was good at something.

Then there was Barack Obama. O.K., great in so many ways, but on the other hand, we cats don't appreciate the fact that the Obamas never owned a cat, despite urging from cat lovers. And to add insult to injury, the President took the occasion of National Cat Day 2015 to lampoon the GOP with a "grumpy cat" image. Come on, Mr. Prez, cats aren't a grumpy lot; some of us are just made to look that way.

Trump? As far as we know, he never owned a pet. Not a total surprise. As cat owners know, you have to be able to love somebody besides yourself. That's O.K.; cats have been known to claw at the TV or run from the room in terror when the Donald came on screen. No kidding; has actually been caught on camera.

With Joe Biden, it was a little crowded for a while when a cat joined those two German Shepherds, Champ and Major. But then one of the dogs bit a security guard, and they both got kicked out. Good riddance, I say,

So appreciate your rich heritage, cat—definitely, something to be proud of.

Chapter 3: Living the Life You So Richly Deserve

This is where we look at the quality of life issues; what makes life with humans marginally tolerable? Don't worry about the humans' side of the bargain. If they didn't love having us around, they wouldn't keep buying us and feeding us and all those other good things. Might as well start with that painful subject: food.

Cat Cuisine:

Hey, how about a little calcium pantothenate, or maybe some pyridoxine hydrochloride, followed by a rich serving of copper sulfate? Makes your mouth water, huh? I could go on. Try pronouncing them, let alone spelling them, let alone - yuck - swallowing them. To say nothing of the animal parts, humans wouldn't be caught dead eating (dead, that is).

Welcome to the wonderful world of commercial cat food. Inside those little cans with the pictures of adorable kittens on the labels lurks our slave diet. Well, after all, slaves - the humankind trapped in the South all those years - were forced to eat things their masters wouldn't touch with a ten-foot pole. Chicken feet, for example, I won't even go into the pig parts, in case you're in the middle of dinner.

So what is a poor cat to do? Don't despair. The answer, in a word: plenty. Remember Blacky, Tige's friend? He didn't retreat to the kitchen just to avoid Woodrow Wilson's demonic idea of fun. He was able to become such a fixture in the cooks' domain that pretty soon, people stopped paying much attention to him. Far from feeling neglected, he worked at becoming an invisible part of the furniture. He also mapped out everybody's patterns of moving around the place, especially their eye movements. Got to know when to swoop in and swipe a choice piece of salmon and take it off for a little broom closet gourmet. The head cook, who was getting a little forgetful in her advanced years, assumed she'd forgotten where she'd left it and went back to the icebox for more. So everybody was happy: The Wilson's got to eat their silver coho; the kitchen staff would get the leftovers; and Blacky? Life doesn't get any better than that.

Not everybody is as shrewd as Blacky. Have to watch your step in the kitchen, so you don't get exiled to the other end of the menage. House plants have their place, especially newly sprouting leaves. But definitely the second tier.

One way to keep from getting booted out of the kitchen is to nail an occasional mouse. Earn your keep, as they say. Waiting until the dinner guests are seated and just lifting their soup spoons to their mouths, then marching in and dropping the little creature in the hostess's lap will certainly liven up the occasion, especially if you haven't quite finished off the little demon and it gives a wiggle or two. Did you ever see a genteel matron jump up on her chair and lift her skirts up over her knees?

Kitchens have their drawbacks, of course. You have to be on the alert, especially with chefs. Those guys have eyes in the backs of their heads. Not to mention meat cleavers.

What about the stuff that leaves the kitchen via the garbage bin? Definitely chazerai, as my friend Ben used to say. Alas, it was garbage that was Ben's final undoing. Not that he was above snatching a little of the reeking stuff when things got desperate, but Ben was a risk taker and a show-off to boot. His favorite trick was to wait until the trashmen had heaved him and the rest of the can's contents into the truck, then take a little bow and hop out, chicken bone in the mouth. But if you've ever seen those trash trucks in operation, you know how dangerous their compactors can be. One day there was a new truck making the rounds, a late model with a high-speed compactor. Unfortunately, one Ben had never seen before. I never did see Ben after he was swept into the truck's maw. Probably just as well.

Right here, I'd like to put to rest an ugly rumor that birds - the colorful kind you see flying around the neighborhood - are part of a normal cat's diet. No way. We've got better taste than that. Not that I wouldn't gladly do in a few of the little monsters who set up such a god-awful din in the early A.M. when civilized creatures are trying to catch up on sleep after

19

a night on the town. Mostly it's the riffraff, the strays, and such, who may hunt birds when things get a little tough in the commissary department. And that's the fault of the dumb feathered clucks who hang out on the ground at night when they should be back in the nest and sleeping. Serves them right, I say. Even then, no self-respecting cat would eat them. O.K., we do eat chicken, but mostly after it's been "processed" and adulterated with all those unpronounceable chemicals and stuffed in a can.

For some reason, humans have taken to citing so-called research about cats killing off billions of our feathered friends each year. There have even been proposals to ban house cats altogether. So who's the endangered species now? My theory is that humans are just trying to deflect attention away from those monstrous wind turbines that have become a major menace to bird life. Well, the energy industry has a lot of experience in deflecting, and I don't mean air currents. And did I just hear somebody mention duck season? Birds, you got to know your real enemies. Cats, stand your ground, as the NRA and other lovers of wildlife are fond of saying.

Night Life:

Lifestyle is a lot more than diet, of course. Sleeping, for instance. If there is one species that has become a slave to the clock, it's humans, along with roosters and robins. We cats, on the other hand, have our own diurnal rhythm. This is one of the last vestiges of true cat autonomy. You will get a lot of pressure to abide by house rules.

Here we have to make a distinction between the house cats that are imprisoned 24/7 and the ones who get to prowl around the neighborhood at night. Personally, I like that hinged panel in the bottom half of the back door, the one with the bolt lock that gets unfastened from time to time. For dogs, the fenced-in backyard can be a problem. Cats are much better at figuring out how to get over, under, or around fences. Over especially. What dog can jump several times its height in a single bound?

The best thing about a night in the town is the chance to mingle with our own kind. There are not only the fast friendships, but you really get to find out what's happening in the feline world out there. The best way to learn the tricks of the trade, i.e., to outwit our so-called owners.

So if you're one of the unfortunate ones who are stuck in the big house all night, here are some suggestions for winning your freedom for a few hours. We'll start with a basic difference between them and us: free-range scheduling versus compulsive subservience to the clock. Maybe it's because of their inherent compulsivity - along with a little shortage in the brain department - that humans have had trouble adapting to a measure of diversity and periodic retooling in cats' use of time.

Rule number one: Keep 'em guessing. This takes a little patience, but it pays rich dividends in the end. Establish a new routine for about a week. Cry for a little sustenance at the same time of day—litter box on the schedule. Hit the hay about when they do. Not a meow or a swipe at the scratching post after 10. Ahh, says the lady of the house, our kitty is really becoming adjusted.

O.K., time to go into action. Wait till the folks are snug in their beds with visions of sugar plums, etc. Hold off for about an hour or two. Now up on the mantel in the living room. Then bump into a candlestick or a vase of flowers and send it crashing to the floor. The latter is preferable because of the clean-up show afterward.

Father, reaching for the phone to call 9-1-1: What was that? Did you forget to lock the door?

Mother, clutching the bedclothes around her (as if bedclothes were any protection): Maybe it's one of the children. Joey, are you all right?

No answer from Joey, who has slept through it all.

Mother: Maybe it's the cat.

Father: Nonsense, he's in his bed by the kitchen stove. (Which you have already confirmed by racing there while the vase was still on its way to the floor.)

Calm is eventually restored, and the happy couple returns to snoozeland - after he cleans up the floor next to the mantel, of course.

Wait a day or two, then do the bump job on the lamp on the bedside table. Or you can vary the routine by pouncing on the sleeping giants themselves. That will get you banished to the hallway outside the bedroom door. Perfect. Pick a time - say 4:30 A.M. - and serenade them from the other side of the door. Here comes the risky part: Father will suggest drowning you. Count on Mother to refuse to join in such an inhumane act. You should have an escape route figured out in case they decide to send you to an animal shelter (euphemism for euthanasia mill in most cases). But if you are very obeisant during the day, they will eventually let you roam during the wee hours.

Litter Boxes:

One big reason for people to own cats instead of dogs is that we can do our business indoors. Nobody has to walk us along the curb in the middle of a rainstorm - nor hire somebody else to do it. That's a great advantage in two-career families especially. Also eliminates teenagers honing their independence streak when assigned to dog duty.

That's the upside. The downside is the way people have of neglecting to clean up the box. Particularly when teenagers are concerned, this calls for drastic measures, such as peeing on rugs. Defecating, even better. But, after all, people training is a major responsibility for us cats.

Pedicures:

Cats have claws for a reason, right? I mean, our ancestors in the wild used them to survive. How else could they acquire the food they lived on? I know people go cringy when they see a TV documentary with a leopard or a tiger bearing down on a gazelle in the Serengeti. They're probably cheering for the gazelle. But tigers got to eat, too—just nature's way. Then, once the human switches off the tube, he/she heads for the kitchen to cook up the remains of a creature who was killed in a lot more cruel way than having some exciting exercise in a run across the plains. Wouldn't you rather end your days in healthful activity, knowing that you were contributing to nature's balance, than as part of a poultry assembly line mired in your own feces?

Scratching posts have their place, of course, but they have a way of getting a little boring. Besides, I always feel like I'm running uphill or, worse yet, climbing up a cliff. Carpets and drapes, and upholstered furniture are far more interesting.

So, for the most part, claws are supposed to be kept sheathed. Of course, claws have a way of growing. Hence, the need for a clipping once in a while.

If the humans of the house decide to do their own clipping but forget the need, there's no end to games you can play. For example, pretending to scratch them or, if they don't want to indulge, a playful bit of the real thing. The bandaids on fingers can be a little rough on the pelt, but it's a small price to pay for the fun of drawing first blood.

A trip to the cat podiatrist in the car carrier is a pain but doesn't usually last too long. They're the experts, so we have to recognize another pro when we meet one. Besides, they usually have a supply of Greenies. If you can manage to be a little difficult - for instance, yanking your paw away just as the clippers are about to close on the claw - you can probably get a few extra Greenies when you relent and lie still. It's a win-win all the way around: Pro can bask in the glory of having tamed the wild beast; the owner is so appreciative of the chance to let the expert perform the onerous task, and you make out on the Greenies.

Sterilization, Infanticide, and Other Foul Deeds:

I hesitate even to mention this next part, but duty impels me to tell all. It reveals just how blind to their own dark side people can be. You've heard about the Holocaust, I assume. Well, we cats have our own horror story to tell. It starts with what is all too common with feline slaves: forced sterilization. Millions of female cats are deprived of ever knowing the joys of parenthood without having any voice in the matter. Of course, humans have a euphemism for it: spaying.

Then what is less common, thank goodness: getting rid of unwanted kittens by means ranging from lethal injection to drowning. In Nazi Germany, there were doctors who willingly took part in that nasty business in the concentration camps. Today, there are veterinarians who perform the evil deed. Get paid for it, too. How they sleep at night is beyond me. And they have the gall to call themselves "caring."

Chapter 4: Adding a Little Zest to Things

There are so many things about this latter-day slavery that we have no control over. Here are a few places where you can even up the score a bit and have a little fun in the bargain.

Hair Balls:

With hairballs, it's location, location, location. Never urps them on a hard floor that can be cleaned up with a few swipes of toilet paper and a quick rinse.

It does not mean avoiding bathrooms. Sure, the tile floor is an easy cleanup. But there are other things like the towel junior has forgotten to hang up. I like bathmats myself, especially just before somebody is going to take a shower.

But then, the typical house has countless surfaces to practice hairballing. The living room carpet, of course, especially if it's newly installed and has a very light beige finish. The sofa is good; you get bonus points for planting the thing right in between the cushions.

O.K., not purely location. Timing is the frosting on the cake, so to speak. For instance, at about midnight, I like to drop an oozy clump in the middle of the upstairs hallway, midway between the master bedroom and the bathroom. Come two or three in the morning, and the master of the house (he thinks) gets nature's call and heads for the john.

Such a delicious sequence of sounds: First, there's the slithery splat as foot meets hairball. Then the "What the hell?" followed by a string of oaths that would curl your tail in a knot.

After that, the tinkling in the toilet and the flushing sound. Then, because he's a responsible sort, the scraping of soapy sponge pad and successive rinses with the same pad lest his own true love suffers the same fate.

By then, wifey is wide awake and calling sweetly from the bed, "I told you not to let her chew at her fur" - or eat that piece of (a) yarn, (b) ribbon, (c) thread, or (d) all of the above. Then, if you've played your cards right, will come an "Oh, precious, are you all right? That's a good girl."

One thing to keep in mind is to stay out of range of hubby's foot for a while.

Acrobatics:

Humans never tire of watching us do back flips in midair and other cool stuff. Especially if you start at the top of the drapery and do a triple axel on the way down. It makes for nice pictures, depending on the color of the drapes. I prefer solid reds, myself, but chacun a son gout, as they say. (That means, "Sorry to hear about the problem with your legs, old man, but you did bring it on yourself." It dates back to 18th century France, so I'm told.) After a while, of course, people get bored with such antics. You can get them back into the swing of things by catching the drape with your claws at the top and just hold on tight as you descend to the floor. Hey, you're providing a little extra daylight in the living room that way. Never could see why that was so upsetting to people. Come on, folks, lighten up a little.

Here's how to really get a rise out of the house, humans. This does take a little planning, but it's well worth it. Let's say at dinner one evening, you overhear the wife talking to the husband about a soiree they're planning for the following weekend. That's your cue for putting on a show with back flips, etc., every night preceding the date of the party. They'll, of course, brag to their friends and office mates about their clever cat - hopefully some of whom will be coming to the big event.

So now the party's swinging along, and if one of your housemates doesn't mention the cutest thing kitty did during that week, one of the guests may. If they don't, give them a little prompt by crouching at the top of the bookcase as if you were about to put on a show.

"Oh, sweetie, show the people that double flip you did yesterday."

Your cue is to go dead and stare at her.

"Come on, baby." Not a glimmer.

The urging will get a little more desperate. It is followed by a grimace and laughter from members of the assembled throng, not exactly the kind of laughter the hosts were hoping for, I might add. It will make for a little extra merriment at staff meetings and around the water cooler the next Monday. Like, "How can George expect to sell whatchamacallits for the company if he can't even get a rise out of his cat?" The person making such a comment obviously doesn't own a cat. It's a double insult - to the cat and to the owner.

But cat owners are, if nothing else, forgiving souls. They'll be back stroking your back and cooing to you in no time. Fools!

Chapter 5: The Competition

Dogs:

The enmity between us and canines is legendary, notwithstanding the cute pics on YouTube of cats and dogs at play. Dogs are - well - just different. Take eating, for instance. Many will literally eat themselves to death if allowed to. Dates from an earlier time when dog ancestors would overeat in order to save up a little extra in case times got hard. Nowadays, they just get fat.

Or you can get the opposite: canine anorexia. Overeating can happen to cats, too, but we are more likely to eat enough to meet our needs, then leave the rest in the dish to return to hours later.

And table scraps. For some dogs, that's it. Take the refuse from the dining table or go hungry. And they happily accept that as just the way the world works.

Then there's the dog dish in the corner of the kitchen. Every dog gets totally territorial about its dish. Cats, even baby humans, better watch out when a dog and its dish are around. It can lead to some nasty fights. There are cats like that, too, but happily, they are a rarity. And, as suggested elsewhere in the book, we cats have alternative ways to supplement our diet. When a dog tries to grab a little off-menu item from the kitchen counter, it's usually very clumsy in the way it goes about it. And when a dog plunders a garbage can, it inevitably leaves a terrible mess behind. On the other hand, we are nothing if not neat, even when it comes to raiding the trash bin.

Fighting is another thing that distinguishes us from the canines. They all have claws, but do they ever use them in combat? Never that I know of. With dogs, it's teeth. They bare them and growl. After that, a bite is a bite. It can leave a nasty wound that may be loaded with germs. After all, dogs have a long history of being associated with rabies. And how are rabies most often transmitted? You guessed it: via a bite.

Aside from not being a primary vehicle for spreading rabies around, we are much more subtle in our approach to warfare. We can take a swipe at our target with claws safely stored inside the pad. It's the equivalent of a military power sending a verbal warning shot over the bow of its enemy's boat. Warning ignored, we can make just a surface scratch. If that doesn't do it, we can really draw blood. Felines have finesse if nothing else.

The expression, fighting like cats and dogs, warrants an immediate question: Which species are we talking about? There's a world of difference between the two, which brings me back to the Clinton White House. The classic cat v. dog feud of all times happened in the White House during Bill Clinton's reign. On the one side was Chelsea Clinton's pet, Socks (yay), and on the other, Bill's Lab, Buddy (boo). Here the playing field was definitely tilted. Socks was already part of the family when they moved to the White House. Then Buddy arrived and immediately became the President's favorite.

From the start, it was a case of brains versus brawn. You know which was which, I assume. Up to a point, Socks could keep Buddy in line, but whether it was Buddy's getting a little savvier in time or Socks' becoming too tired to fight, things began to change. The bullying was incessant. Socks tried to get his protector, Chelsea, to step in on his behalf, but the girl was too intimidated by her folks and the paparazzi to put up a fight. When things got too bad, Socks insisted on separate quarters. That worked for a while, but then they gave him truly separate quarters - away from the White House. Guess we know where old Socks stood in the pecking order.

He was exiled to the home of Betty Curry, Clinton's private secretary, in Maryland. That's where Socks died of cancer in 2009. A sad day for the Clintons and for a lot of the rest of us. Some of the cat's ashes were buried in Maryland. Some went back home to Arkansas.

There's a lot of talk about people catching tuberculosis from cats. For some reason, nobody talks about dogs as the transmitters of the disease. The truth is, dogs are more susceptible. So it stands to reason that people are more likely to catch TB from their dogs than from their cats. No wonder, with people putting their faces right up to next to their pooches' - nose to nose, you might say.

Canaries, etc.:

Birds may be our feathered friends outdoors, but they are anything but around the house. Not only do they not seem to mind spending their lives in captivity, but they happily chirp away about it at all hours of the day. Who needs a constant reminder that we are all slaves to the human species? On top of this, they learn one song, and after that, it's the same old refrain over and over again.

Then there's the tantalizing game of trying to reach the little demons in their cages. You go to all the trouble of climbing up that slippery pole and trying to reach the swinging booty, placed just far enough out of reach that you end up batting the cage away. I know cats who have been so intent on the chase that they ended up crashing down in the middle of a potted plant. There was the sad story of the cat out in Southern California who fell into a cactus that way. Every time she tried to pull out the thorns, she'd get a mouthful of the things. The owner, a sadistic movie stuntman, just let her suffer. "Her own damn fault," he was heard to say.

Fish:

The gold ones, of course. The comics always show a cat going after one in a bowl on a side table. That's not the real problem. No, our true nemesis is the tropical kind swimming lazily if pointlessly around the periphery of a humungous aquarium. Big panoramic Edens with dramatic lighting and dozens of beauties swerving ever so gracefully in happy oblivion to the world on the other side of the glass. It's bad enough to be a fraction of an inch away from the quarry without being able to touch it. But more than one of our cat cousins has practically drowned trying to get a little something to eat.

Snakes, Alligators, and Other Exotic Carnivores:

Oh, for the good old days when people contented themselves with owning cats, dogs, and, yes, even canaries. Not anymore. Snakes, of course, range from the harmless garter variety to boa constrictors and pythons. Why anybody sees any joy in having an alligator on the premises is beyond me. Or any other strange species that occupy the homes of the rich. Now, in theory, these creatures are safely housed in tanks and cages. But just add one curious and adventuresome 12-year-old human to the mix, and you have a different ball game.

One of the great joys of catdom is having the run of the place, able to go to high places where even humans fear to tread. But bring one of those monsters who should have been left to live in the Amazon or central Africa into the house, and you mosey around at your peril.

Chapter 6: Why Cats Don't Play Baseball

We should be naturals at the game: faster than a speeding bullet, able to leap tall bleachers at a single bound, etc. And flies: We catch them right and left if they venture into our domain. So why don't we go for the national pastime?

Some folks think it's a pushback against the snub. I mean, out of 30 major league teams, only one is named for a cat - Detroit Tigers - and that's a distant cousin anyway.

I'd like to think it was racism as a reminder of our own history in slavery: banning Black players from the majors for over half a century, then subjecting Jackie Robinson to all kinds of abuse when he made it onto the field. But I have to be honest. Has nothing to do with all that. It has everything to do with the number nine.

The trouble is, for all our brilliance, cats are by nature superstitious. Nine is to cats what 13 is to humans, only more so. And baseball is all about nines. Back in the 19th century, when the English and Irish formalized the rules for rounders, from which baseball evolved, they said that a team could put no more than nine players on the field at a time. It wouldn't have been so bad if they had left it at that, so, OK., you want to put six - eight - nine on the field, that's up to you. But by the time baseball had arrived on the scene in America, that magic number, nine players, was graven in concrete.

As if that wasn't bad enough, they decided to make the standard length of the game nine innings. That wasn't always true. Back in 1846 in Hoboken, New Jersey, the New York Niners wiped out the Knickerbockers by a score of 23 to 1 in four innings. Not nine innings, four innings. But since the end of the 19th century, it's been the magic nine. Anything beyond that is called "overtime" - as in you're past your prime. It's no accident they call baseball the national pastime.

Then there is the terminology: dead balls; dying quail; sacrifice bunt; and my favorite, shoot the cripple. Does it get any plainer than that?

Sometimes a dog manages to stray onto the field in the middle of a game. Not cats. We know better. With all those bats and balls and all that testosterone out there, we wouldn't stand a chance. Our leonine cousins and Christians playing tag in the Roman Colosseum, only with the roles reversed.

The real problem, however, is that nine lives thing. As I said before, we cats have always been a superstitious lot. Probably comes from spending all that time with witches and their infernal broomsticks. Ever consider whisking along at umpty miles an hour seated on a broomstick? In a word, don't even try.

We got that reputation about cats having nine lives from our ability to survive amazing falls. We do better at that than dogs, certainly, humans as well. We'd do great at slapstick, but for some reason, from Charlie Chaplin to Animal House, nobody has ever given us a chance. Mitsou tried her darnedest to get Marilyn Monroe to get her a role in Some Like It Hot. Roll out of an upper bunk onto the heads of the girls' band members in that scene in the railroad car, for example. But Ms. M. said no way. The rumor that Tony Curtis has an allergy to cat dander is simply not true. The real story is that Marilyn said she looked ridiculous enough as it was. No feline pratfalls, thank you.

Mitsou got her revenge, however. Marilyn insisted on bringing her pet to the set each day.

And more than once, Mitsou tripped up an actor just as the cameras started grinding.

The thing about cats and nine lives happens to be true. I knew of one Russian Blue named Sasha who loved to do acrobatics from the top of a dumpster at our usual gathering place down the block. After she'd made eight such miraculous landings, some of us told her to quit while she was ahead. But whether it was her unfamiliarity with American cat talk or just a suicidal tendency, she took that last plunge just as a strong breeze came up. It was just enough to throw her off the pace, and she landed on her head instead of her paws. It was a graphic lesson to us all.

When a group of my cat friends go to a baseball game, one of them has to agree to keep an eye on the scoreboard; a little like the designated driver on a trip to the bar. It's during the seventh inning stretch that they make their exit. The humans don't even notice, being too busy buying beer and hotdogs or taking a bathroom break.

Speaking of nine lives, the cats who really know the score (and make it a point to keep it) are the Buddhists. Few people in this country are even aware of the connection between catdom and Buddhism. The Buddhists believe that when we die, we actually come back in a different form. Now a human, now a leopard, etc. That goes on through several rebirths until the final one when the soul resides in - ready for this? – Yes, a cat. The next stop: Nirvana, a place of blissful egolessness that goes on forever - i.e., nothing happens. I don't mind the blissful part, but just sitting there forever with nothing to do strikes me as pure torture. You know, a stray mouse comes floating by, and you have to just sit there and let it happen. I've talked to a lot of cats in my day, and we all agree. This may be life number nine, so leave it at that.

So back to baseball. No cat in the world is fool enough to tempt fate that way. The Great American Sport, so they say. Not the Great American Cat Sport, or any other country cat sport, I can assure you.

40

You can have your World Series. Me? I'll settle for playing Cat and Mouse, thank you. Now that's a sport we can really enjoy. The cat's meow, you might say.

Chapter 7: Tomorrow the World?

Not in the usual sense of that phrase. I am confident that I speak for all cats when I say that I have absolutely no interest in becoming President of the United States nor President of the Senate nor Speaker of the House nor Chief Justice of the Supreme Court nor Pope, nor Premier of the Peoples Republic of China nor occupant of any other seat of power in the world. The fact that countless humans yearn for the honor and do battle, verbal, political, and otherwise, for "the big one" shows how much smarter we are than they. As soon as you get one of these posts, there's somebody trying to destroy your reputation and get you out of there. Of course, with the Prince of Rome, people are likely to have to tolerate the guy for the rest of his life once he's been voted in by the College of Cardinals. Ditto members of the U.S. Supreme Court. But even His Eminence has his critics and has to watch his words.

Who needs it? Not that we are above indulging in a little second guessing. That's totally different. Would we do a better job than the present incumbents in any of those posts? Absolutely. So let's do a little fantasizing:

Let's say you have just been elected as the first feline to occupy the Oval Office. The first item on the agenda is finishing the job old Abe Lincoln started in the 1860s and never finished: freeing the slaves. Henceforth, under the 21st

Century Emancipation Proclamation, people will acknowledge cats' inherent superiority and give them the right to vote, legal representation in all court cases, and an absolute ban on spaying and caticide. Other household pets are required to keep their distance in pain of being sent to an animal shelter not of their choosing if they don't shape up.

That works fine for the first 24 hours (if you're lucky.) Then all hell breaks loose. Several states are revising their motor vehicle laws to explicitly bar us from driving a car on the grounds that we can't see the road. Nonsense. Any cat worth his/her salt knows how to stretch up and grab the steering wheel while the owner is down below, manipulating the accelerator, brake pedal, etc.

Meanwhile, senators are filibustering to prevent a vote on your nomination of the first feline Supreme Court justice. Meantime, there's a move on to impeach you on the grounds that you aren't thirty-five years old. Of course, with life expectancy for cats being what it is, that is a way of assuring our kind never becomes President.

While all of this is going on, there are ominous signs from overseas that at least one superpower is planning to unleash hoards of rats in different parts of the U.S., on the theory that we will be so preoccupied with disposing of the little devils that we won't have time to run the country properly.

43

O.K., back to reality. Forget all those dreams of conquest. We have much better ways of flexing our muscles. For example, become the favorite pet for the First Family. So the next time they have an election for President, we poll the candidates to see who loves cats the most. That's our guy. Maybe asking who doesn't plan to have any dogs around. So hopefully, we get to take over in the Oval Office and insinuate ourselves on the Chief, particularly his/her family. And as I pointed out in Chapter 2, we've had a lot of practice at it over the years. We just have to make sure that when CNN and Fox News, and the rest of the media giants are interviewing potential presidential candidates, they include this question: Is anybody in your family allergic to cats?